SIMPLIFYING ELECTRICITY

through the Unifact method is designed to teach you all the essentials of electricity with maximum efficiency. In small, concise steps it covers: the nature of electricity, electric currents at work, basic electric circuits, Ohm's Law, resistance in series, resistance in parallel, electric power, fuses and power load, generating electric current, magnetism and electromagnetism, magnetic force and electric generators.

THE MOST EFFECTIVE WAY YET DESIGNED FOR LEARNING THE BASIC PRINCIPLES OF ELECTRICITY!

SIMPLIFYING ELECTRICITY
BY BRADLEY V. SMITH

A UNIFACT BOOK

A PROGRAMMED TEXT

SIMPLIFYING ELECTRICITY
Bantam Unifact edition published November 1966

Library of Congress Catalog Card Number: 66–23653

Published simultaneously in the United States and Canada.

Bantam Books are published by Bantam Books, Inc., a subsidiary
of Grosset & Dunlap, Inc. Its trade-mark, consisting of the words
"Bantam Books" and the portrayal of a bantam, is registered in the
United States Patent Office and in other countries. Marca Registrada.
Bantam Books, Inc., 271 Madison Avenue, New York, N.Y. 10016.

PRINTED IN THE UNITED STATES OF AMERICA

CONTENTS

To the Reader 7

Acknowledgments 8

How to Use This Unifact Text 9

THE NATURE OF ELECTRICITY 12

Electron Shells 18

Static Electricity 24

Static Electricity and Force 30

ELECTRIC CURRENTS AT WORK 37

BASIC ELECTRIC CIRCUITS 44

OHM'S LAW 50

Resistances in Series 57

Resistances in Parallel 62

ELECTRIC POWER 70

Fuses and Power Loads 76

GENERATING ELECTRIC CURRENT 84

MAGNETISM AND ELECTROMAGNETISM . . . 92

Bar Magnets 92

Magnetic Force 100

Electromagnetism 105

Electric Generators 115

TO THE READER

Learning is easiest when it is acquired in small increments
... and reinforced by repetition.

This text develops the essentials of electrical theory in small,
concise steps. Each frame contains a single idea. Each new idea
is followed by an example. Each example is reinforced by quiz
questions.

Explanations are simple and compact, enabling you to keep
the key idea in sharp focus. Key ideas are purposely repeated.
Each repetition, in turn, develops an expansion of the initial
concept.

Learning is further reinforced by the text's self-quiz structure. Spot Checks, following each new discussion, repeat the
text material and give the reader a quick report on his progress.
To the reader who has followed the text, step by step, the
answers to the Spot Check questions are obvious. This obvious-
ness is an indication of successful learning ... of new informa-
tion and concepts acquired without conscious effort.

The Spot Checks are also progress reports. Each question is
keyed to the frame which explains the idea the question checks.
Thus, any weakness the quiz discloses can be instantly
remedied.

Answers to the Spot Checks will always be found on the
following lefthand page.

ACKNOWLEDGMENTS

The author gratefully acknowledges his debt to Mr. Bertram Siegal, Chairman of the Science Department, Bedford Junior High School, Westport, Connecticut, and to Dr. Thomas R. Jennings, Assistant Professor of Physics, Queensboro Community College, City University of New York—both of whom reviewed this manuscript in its formative state, and whose criticism and suggestions have contributed much to its competence.

HOW TO USE THIS UNIFACT TEXT

i. **Where should we begin?**

   With Frame No. 1.

ii. **But Frame No. 1 is obvious. Can't we skip to some place where the going gets tough?**

   No.

iii. **Why not?**

   Because if we read every frame carefully, the going will never get tough.

iv. **But isn't it tiresome to read what we already know?**

   The purpose of this book is not to entertain, but to teach the basic facts of electrical theory—simply, directly, and painlessly.

v. **After reading the first frame, what next?**

   Continue to the first Spot Check. Don't skip.

vi. How are the Spot Checks to be used?

Try to answer every question correctly. Fill in the blanks (or write answers on a separate sheet of paper), then check all answers against the text answers (which are printed on the next lefthand page).

vii. What if some of our answers are wrong?

Return to the frame indicated opposite each Spot Check question missed. The frame will tell us what we did wrong.

viii. When can we move on to a new section?

When we have been able to answer every question correctly in the preceding Spot Check.

ix. Is it necessary to progress so slowly?

Learning is easy if we learn one fact at a time—and learn it thoroughly—before moving on to the next. We make the greatest progress slowly . . . with constant repetition of key ideas. This is the psychological basis of the UNIFACT method.

x. Doesn't the text contain many repetitions?

It does. The repetitions have been carefully planned and tested.

xi. Why?

Because repetitions emphasize a fact and fix it in the mind. Repetitions are the key to efficient learning.

xii. Summarizing: What are the basic rules for using this text?

    1. Don't skip.
    2. Read every frame.
    3. Master every question in every Spot Check.

xiii. What can we expect as a result?

To acquire easily—with minimum effort—a thorough understanding of the basic principles of electricity.

THE NATURE OF ELECTRICITY

1. **If we want to find out anything about the nature of electricity, what is the first thing we have to learn?**

   Something about the behavior of electrons.

2. **Why do we have to learn about electrons to understand electricity?**

   Because all electric activities are basically effects of the piling up or the movement of electrons (just as cloud formations, rain, rivers, etc., are basically the effects of the piling up or flow of water molecules).

3. **What do we mean by an electric current?**

   A flow of electrons along or through a conductor.

4. **What do we mean by an electric charge?**

   Either a piling up of electrons on some surface (this is called a negative charge—as will be explained later); or a shortage of electrons on some surface (this is called a positive charge).

5. **Why do we call an excess, or piling up, of electrons a negative charge?**

   Because electrons are regarded as negative particles; therefore, adding electrons to a surface gives the surface an excess of negative particles.

6. **How can we cause a surface to have a positive charge?**

> By removing electrons from the surface—thus causing the surface to have a shortage of electrons.

---

7. **When electrons are added to a neutral surface, what kind of charge does the surface acquire?**

> A negative charge.

---

8. **When electrons are removed from a neutral surface, what kind of charge would we expect to find on the surface?**

> A positive charge.

---

9. **We have talked about an electric current and electric charges in terms of electrons, but what is an electron?**

> Negative atomic particles which are thought to be moving about the center, or nucleus, of an atom.
>
> (Note: This electron movement is often referred to as circling or orbiting since early models of the atom assumed that electrons rotated about the nucleus much as the moon or artificial satellites move about the earth—in fixed orbits. Recent theory assumes only movement about the nucleus without any clearly defined path—much as a molecule in a cloud of gas might move about an object located in the center of the cloud.)

---

10. **What is the general structure of an atom?**

> A nucleus, or center, around which electrons are assumed to move.

---

11. Do all atoms have the same structure?

Yes—but the number of particles in the nucleus, and the number of electrons that move around the nucleus, are not the same in atoms of different substances. (But all atoms of the same substance have approximately the same structure.)

12. The atom of what element has the simplest structure?

Hydrogen—the hydrogen atom has only one electron moving about the nucleus.

13. What is a proton?

A particle that is said to have a positive charge.

14. In what part of an atom would we expect to find protons?

In the nucleus (center).

15. How many protons are in an atom?

Normally, there are the same number of protons and electrons. Thus, there are the same number of equal positive and negative particles . . . and an atom is electrically neutral.

16. Can an atom receive a positive charge?

Yes. If an atom loses an electron, it then has more protons (positive particles) than electrons (negative particles). The atom is then said to have a positive charge.

17. What happens to an atom when it gains an electron?

It acquires a negative charge.

18. Diagram the structure of an atom.

In the diagram below we see the relation of parts of the hydrogen atom, whose nucleus is a single proton. The shell of the hydrogen atom consists of a single electron moving around the nucleus.

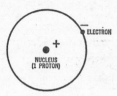

19. Do some atoms have more complex structures?

Yes. The atoms of all the elements, other than hydrogen, consist of a nucleus made up of many protons (and other particles called neutrons). This nucleus is surrounded by shells (energy levels) of orbiting electrons. There is normally one electron in orbit for every proton in the nucleus.

1. It is necessary to know something about the behavior of electrons if we want to understand the nature of

   _____.

   _____[1]

2. All _____ activities are essentially effects of the _____ or the _____ electrons.

   _____[2]

3. A flow of electrons along or through a conductor is what we mean by the term _____.

   _____[3]

4. A piling up of electrons on some surface, or a shortage of electrons on some surface, is called a(n) _____.

   _____[4]

5. Because electrons are regarded as negative atomic particles, an excess of electrons on a surface gives that surface a _____.

   _____[7]

6. Negative atomic particles which are regarded as moving about the nucleus of an atom are called _____.

   _____[9]

7. It is assumed that all atoms have a structure which consists of a _____, or center, around which _____ orbit.

   _____[10]

8. The atoms of some elements (elementary substances) contain more orbiting _____, and more particles in the _____, than do the atoms of other elements.

_____[11]

9. The hydrogen atom has the simplest structure, because in the hydrogen atom only _____ electron moves about the nucleus.

_____[12]

10. In the following diagram of a hydrogen atom, label the part that represents the electron.

_____[18]

11. The atoms of all the elements other than hydrogen have more than _____ electron moving about the nucleus.

_____[19]

For answers, see page 18

ELECTRON SHELLS

---

20. **Name two elements whose atoms have many electrons orbiting around the nucleus.**

    Copper, whose atoms contain 29 electrons; iron, whose atoms contain 26 electrons.

---

21. **If an atom contains a great many electrons, do all of these orbit at the same distance from the nucleus?**

    No. The orbits of electrons form "shells," or energy levels, each of which may be filled. The outer shell of some atoms (such as copper) may not be filled.

---

22. **Why is the outer shell of an atom important in the study of electric activity?**

    If the outer shell is less than half-filled, some of the electrons in this shell can be detached, or stripped away from the atom. An atom whose outer shell is less than half-filled can give up some or all of these electrons.

18

23. If the outer shell of an atom is more than half-filled, do the electrons in this shell become more tightly bound to the atom?

Yes. We could compare the behavior of these electrons to books in a tightly packed shelf of a bookcase. The tighter the packing, the harder it is to dislodge a single book.

---

24. Is there a special name for electrons that are only loosely bound to the nucleus of some atoms?

Yes. Free electrons.

---

25. Do the atoms of all elements contain the same number of free electrons?

No. There are more free electrons in the atoms of some elements than others. Metals contain more free electrons than do elements like silicon and sulfur.

---

26. What makes a substance a good conductor of electricity?

The fact that the outer shell of each of its atoms is less than half-filled and consequently contains loosely bound or free electrons. We have seen (Frame 22) that if the outer shell is less than half-filled, the electrons in this shell are only loosely bound to the nucleus (that is, are free electrons).

---

27. Give some examples of substances that are good conductors of electricity (because atoms of these substances have many electrons that are loosely bound or free). [See diagrams on following page.]

Copper, silver, gold, aluminum . . . in fact, all metals.

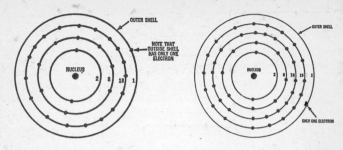

Diagram showing number
of electrons in each shell
of an atom of copper.

Diagram showing number
of electrons in each shell
of an atom of silver.

28. What is an insulator?

A substance whose atoms have an outer shell which
is more than half-filled with electrons. These electrons are tightly bound to the nucleus (hence, not
free) and the atom consequently offers great opposition to free electron flow. Examples: glass, rubber,
mica, bakelite, sulfur.

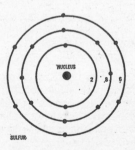

Here is a diagram showing the number of electrons in each shell
of the sulfur atom. Note that the outer shell, containing 6 electrons, is almost filled. (The third shell of an atom is filled when
it contains 8 electrons.)

29. Is there any perfect insulator?

No. All substances conduct to a greater or lesser extent—at ordinary temperatures. Some substances, however, like glass, mica, rubber, asbestos, and bakelite are such poor conductors that they can be regarded as insulators.

30. Are there any perfect conductors—at ordinary temperatures?

No. All substances, at ordinary temperatures, offer some resistance to the passage of an electric current. The best conductor (the substance having the lowest resistance) is silver. After silver (in the order named) are copper, aluminum, brass, zinc, and iron.

31. Are free electrons important, in electric theory, only because they account for the behavior of conductors of an electric current?

No. They are also important because they account for the generating of an electric current and the existence of an electric charge.

32. What is the relation between free electrons and the generating of an electric current?

As will be seen later, free electrons removed from atoms of certain elements can be induced to flow along or through conductors. Batteries and generators are devices that play a part in causing electric currents by channeling such electrons into a steady flow through conductors.

1. The atoms of copper and iron are examples of atoms which have many _____ orbiting around a _____.
   _____[20]

2. In atoms that contain many electrons, all of the electrons are not orbiting at the same _____ from the _____.
   _____[21]

3. The fact that electrons in a shell that is less than half-filled can be stripped away from the atom has a fundamental bearing on the theory of _____.
   _____[22]

4. Electrons in a shell that is _____ than half-filled tend to behave like books on a tightly packed shelf of a bookcase.
   _____[23]

5. Free electrons are electrons that are only _____ to the _____ of some atoms.
   _____[24]

6. Metals contain more _____ than elements such as silicon and sulfur.
   _____[25]

7. Substances made up of elements whose atoms contain _____ are good conductors of _____.
   _____[26]

8. A substance composed of elements whose outer shell is filled or nearly filled is called a(n) _____.

_____[28]

9. Although all substances conduct an electric current to some extent, substances like glass, mica, rubber, and asbestos are such poor conductors that they are called

_____.

_____[29]

10. Even the best conductors, at ordinary temperatures, offer some _____ to the passage of an electric current.

_____[30]

11. To explain how an electric current is generated, it is necessary to account for the nature and behavior of _____.

_____[31]

12. Batteries and generators are devices that generate an electric current by removing free electrons from the atoms of certain substances and inducing these electrons to flow through _____.

_____[32]

13. Electrons are particles with a _____ charge, and protons are particles with a _____ charge.

_____[9, 13]

1. Electrons, nucleus
2. Distance, nucleus
3. Electricity
4. More
5. Loosely bound, nucleus
6. Free electrons
7. Free electrons, electric current (or electricity)
8. Insulator
9. Insulators
10. Resistance
11. Free electrons
12. Conductors
13. Negative, positive

STATIC ELECTRICITY

33. What name is commonly given to a flow of free electrons?

Electric current.

34. What results when free electrons accumulate on a surface?

A negative charge.

35. If some free electrons are removed from a surface, what is the result?

The surface has a positive charge.

36. Putting these facts together, what can we say is the basic difference between an electric current and an electric charge?

An electric current is characterized by free electrons in motion. An electric charge is an excess or shortage of free electrons on a surface.

37. **What common English word means "not moving," or "at rest"?**

   Static.

---

38. **What term in electric theory is used to describe the behavior of free electrons which pile up (or exist in relatively insufficient numbers) on a surface?**

   Static electricity.

---

39. **What is a spark?**

   The visible discharge or movement of free electrons (from a surface that has relatively more free electrons than the surface onto which they move).

---

40. **What is lightning?**

   A large spark.

---

41. **Define an electric charge.**

   The condition of a surface which results from the accumulation on that surface of an excess of free electrons, or from a relative deficiency of free electrons.

---

42. **What do we call a charge that results from an accumulation, or excess, of electrons?**

   A negative charge.

---

43. Why "negative"?

> Because electrons are atomic particles that are said to be *negative*. (The term is used to show a difference in behavior from other atomic particles, such as protons, which are said to be *positive*.) Thus, a surface which accumulates negative particles gains a negative charge.

44. Since "negative" means the opposite of "positive," what charge would we say a surface has if it loses free electrons?

> Positive.

45. If a wave momentarily piles up more water on one side of a tank than on the other, what will the piled up water tend to do (after the wave passes)?

> Flow back toward the side of the tank having less water. Specifically, the tendency is to restore equilibrium in the tank.

46. If water is momentarily piled up on one side of a tank, what condition then exists on the opposite side of the tank?

> It has, relatively, a deficiency or shortage of water.

47. What name is given to the electric condition created by a deficiency of electrons?

> Positive charge.

48. When a glass rod is rubbed with a piece of silk, some of the free electrons are rubbed off the rod and transferred to the silk. What kind of charge does the silk then have?

> Negative . . . because the silk has acquired an excess of negative particles (free electrons).

49. After the glass rod has been rubbed with the silk, does it have an excess or deficiency of free electrons?

A deficiency.

50. Thus, what kind of charge would it have?

A positive charge.

51. What charge would there be on the silk?

A negative charge.

1. *Electric current* is a term referring to a stream of
   _____.

   _____[33]

2. The term *negative charge* refers to an _____ of free
   electrons on a surface.

   _____[34]

3. A surface is said to have a positive charge if it has a
   relative _____ of free electrons.

   _____[35]

4. The difference between an electric current and an electric
   _____ is basically a difference between free electrons
   in motion and an excess or _____ of free electrons
   on a particular surface.

   _____[36]

5. The English word *static* means _____, or _____.

   _____[37]

6. Static electricity refers to the behavior of _____
   which pile up on, or represent a relative deficiency on
   a surface.

   _____[38]

7. A _____ is the visible discharge or movement of
   free electrons from a surface that has relatively too many
   to a surface that has relatively _____.

   _____[39]

8. Lightning is a _____.

   _____[40]

9. The state of a surface which contains an excess or a deficiency of free electrons is called a _____.

   _____[41]

10. When a surface has an excess of free electrons, we say that the surface has a _____.

_____[42]

11. Electrons are atomic particles which are _____; therefore an excess of free electrons on a surface gives that surface a _____ charge.

_____[43]

12. A surface that loses some of its free electrons is said to have a _____.

_____[44]

13. What electric condition on a surface corresponds to a deficiency of water at one side of a tank? _____

_____[47]

14. If one side of a tank has more water piled up, momentarily, than the opposite side, the side with more water is in a condition that corresponds roughly (in electric theory) to a _____ charge.

_____[47]

15. If a glass rod is rubbed with a piece of silk, some of the _____ on the surface of a glass rod are taken from the rod and transferred to the silk.

_____[48]

16. In the preceding example, the glass rod is left with a _____ of free electrons.

_____[49]

17. The glass rod has acquired a _____ charge.

_____[50]

18. The silk, in this operation, acquires a(n) _____ of free electrons.

_____[42]

19. The silk, thus, acquires a _____ charge.

_____[51]

29

1. Free electrons
2. Accumulation (or piling up)
3. Deficiency
4. Charge, shortage (or deficiency)
5. Not moving, at rest
6. Free electrons
7. Spark, too few
8. Large spark
9. Charge
10. Negative charge
11. Negative, negative
12. Positive charge
13. A positive charge
14. Negative
15. Free electrons
16. Deficiency
17. Positive
18. Excess
19. Negative

STATIC ELECTRICITY AND FORCE

52. If we suspend two small pith balls side by side (as shown in the illustration below) and touch each with a positively charged glass rod (one that has been just rubbed with silk), the pith balls will also become positively charged (because they will give up some of their electrons to the rod). How will the balls then react?

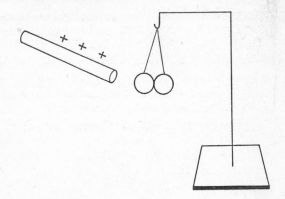

The pith balls repel each other.

(NOTE: Pith is a substance found in the stems of some plants.)

53. Why do the pith balls repel each other?

Because the pith balls are both positively charged, and like charges repel each other.

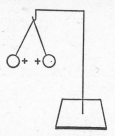

54. Let us try another experiment. If we rub a hard rubber comb with a piece of fur, what will happen? (Remember the glass rod and silk.)

In this case some of the free electrons on the fur will be detached and transferred to the comb.

55. What kind of charge would the comb then have?

A negative charge, because it would then have an excess of free electrons (and the fur would be left with a positive charge).

56. If we now touch one of the pith balls with the negatively charged comb, and the other with the positively charged glass rod, what happens?

The two pith balls move toward each other.

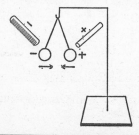

57. Why?

Because, although like charges repel each other, unlike charges attract each other.

58. Do you think these pith balls would attract each other if they were 5 feet apart?

No, because the distance would be too great.

59. Would the pith balls attract each other with the same force no matter how many excess electrons were piled up on the surface of the negatively charged ball?

No. The force (attraction) would be greater as the quantity of electrons increases.

60. What two factors determine the amount of attraction (or repulsion) that exists between two charged bodies—that is, the force of the attraction (or repulsion)?

The amount of charge involved . . . and the distance separating the two charged bodies.

61. What law is used to calculate the amount of attraction (or repulsion) between two charged bodies?

Coulomb's Law, which states that charged bodies attract or repel each other with a force that is directly proportional to the product of the charges and inversely proportional to the square of the distance between them. The law is named after its discoverer, the French engineer and chemist, Charles Augustin de Coulomb (1736–1806).

62. Express Coulomb's Law in the form of an equation.

$$F = \frac{Q \times Q'}{d^2}$$

Where Q and Q' represent the respective charges, d the distance separating the charged bodies, and F the force acting on the two bodies.

63. What unit is used to measure an electric charge?

The unit of electric charge—or, more specifically, the unit quantity of excess electrons—is the *coulomb*. (The coulomb is defined as a charge, on a single body, of 6.28×10^{18} free electrons.)

64. Can an electric current be measured in terms of coulombs?

Yes. The total amount of charge transferred by moving electrons is measured in terms of coulombs . . . but the rate at which the charge is transferred (that is, the rate at which the free electrons move) is measured in amperes.

65. What is an ampere?

A unit of measurement of the rate of flow of moving electrons in a conductor. Because what we call an electric current is actually a movement of free electrons in a conductor, an ampere is a unit used to measure the quantity of electrons passing a point in a given length of time.

(NOTE: The ampere was named in honor of the French physicist André Marie Ampère [1775–1836], who discovered some of the basic principles of electricity and magnetism.)

66. What is the relation of an ampere to a coulomb?

An ampere is equal to one coulomb passing a given point per second.

1. If two small pith balls are suspended side by side, and both are touched by a glass rod that has just been rubbed with silk, the balls will _____ each other.

   _____[52]

2. This action occurs because if two objects are given the same charge, the charges will tend to _____ each other.

   _____[53]

3. If we rub a hard rubber comb with a piece of fur, some of the _____ are detached from the fur and transferred to the comb.

   _____[54]

4. After being rubbed with fur, we say the comb then has a _____ charge.

   _____[55]

5. If we suspend two small pith balls side by side (but separated), then touch one with a positively charged object and the other with a negatively charged object, the two balls will move _____ each other.

   _____[56]

6. Unlike charges _____ each other.

   _____[57]

7. The force between two charged bodies depends on the amount of charge involved and the _____ separating the two charged bodies.

   _____[60]

8. The law used to determine the amount of attraction or repulsion between two charged bodies is called _____ Law.

_____[61]

9. This law, expressed as an equation, is

$$F = \frac{Q \times Q'}{d^2}$$

where $F =$ _____,

Q and $Q' =$ _____,

$d =$ _____.

_____[62]

10. The unit used to measure an electric charge is called the

_____.

_____[63]

11. In dealing with electric currents, we are often more concerned with the rate of flow of free electrons than we are with a total charge held at some point. The unit we use to measure rate of flow of free electrons (that is, the rate at which a charge is transferred from one point to another)

is called the _____.

_____[64]

12. An _____ (the unit used to measure rate of flow of free electrons) is equal to one _____ passing a given point per second.

_____[66]

1. Repel
2. Repel
3. Free electrons
4. Negative
5. Toward
6. Attract

7. Distance
8. Coulomb's
9. Force, respective charges, distance
10. Coulomb
11. Ampere
12. Ampere, coulomb

ELECTRIC CURRENTS AT WORK

67. What do we call the force (per unit area) which makes water or other fluids flow through a pipe?

Pressure.

68. What do we call the energy which makes an electric current flow through a conductor?

Electric pressure or electromotive force (e.m.f.).

69. How do we measure the pressure of a fluid in a pipe?

In pounds per square inch (or similar units, such as grams per square centimeter).

70. How do we measure the electric pressure or electromotive force (e.m.f.) which makes an electric current flow through a conductor?

In volts.

71. What is an electric circuit?

The complete path of an electric current, leaving one side of the source of the electric energy (such as a battery); and returning to the other side of the source. The term *circuit* usually includes both the source of the current and the load (the equipment —such as lamps, heaters, motors—and the controls) activated by the current.

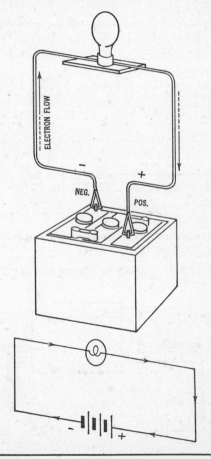

72. Describe a simple piping system that would correspond to a basic electric circuit.

A water pump connected by a pipe to a swimming pool . . . and a return pipe leading back to the pump.

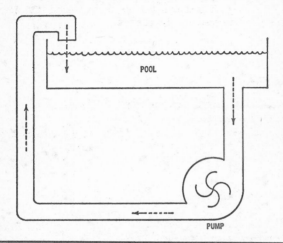

73. What tends to slow down the flow of fluid through a level pipe line?

A resistance, such as friction between the pipe and the fluid.

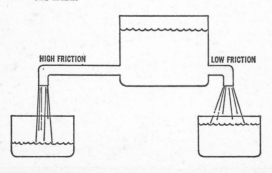

74. **What do we call the "friction" or opposition to the flow of current in an electric circuit?**

Resistance.

75. **What unit is used to measure resistance in an electric circuit?**

The ohm.

(NOTE: The ohm was named after the German physicist Georg Simon Ohm [1787–1854], who discovered the basic relationships in an electric circuit.)

76. **How do we measure the quantity of fluid that passes through a pipe at a given pressure?**

In units describing rate of flow, such as gallons per minute.

77. **What corresponds in an electric circuit to the flow of fluid through a pipe?**

The flow of free electrons (electric current) through a conductor.

78. **What unit of measurement is used for the flow of electrons (electric current) through an electric circuit?**

The ampere.

79. **What is a volt?**

The unit used to measure electric pressure (electromotive force).

80. What is an ohm?

The unit used to measure electric resistance.

81. What is the relationship of a volt, an ampere, and an ohm?

A volt is the force required to "push" one ampere of current through a resistance of one ohm.

82. What name has been given to the law that expresses this relationship?

Ohm's Law.

83. Express Ohm's Law mathematically.

$E = IR$

where E = electromotive force in volts,
$\quad I$ = intensity of the current in amperes,
$\quad R$ = resistance in ohms.

1. To force water to flow through a level pipe it is necessary to apply _____ to the water.

   _____[67]

2. The energy which makes an electric current flow through (or along) a conductor is called _____ force, or electric pressure.

   _____[68]

3. Units such as pounds per square inch or grams per square centimeter are used to measure the _____ of water or other fluids in a pipe.

   _____[69]

4. The energy which makes an electric current flow through a conductor is measured in _____.

   _____[70]

5. The movement of a fluid through a level pipe line tends to be held back by the effect of _____ between the fluid and the inner surface of the pipe.

   _____[73]

6. The ohm is a unit used to measure _____ in an electric circuit.

   _____[75]

7. Units of measurement such as gallons per minute are used to indicate the _____ of flow of fluids through pipes or other conveying devices.

   _____[76]

8. Corresponding roughly to the flow of fluids through a pipe is the flow of _____ through (or along) an electric conductor.

_____[77]

9. The _____ is the unit of measurement for the rate of flow of an electric current.

_____[78]

10. A volt can be defined as the energy (or pressure) required to make one _____ of current pass through a resistance of one _____.

_____[81]

11. The unit used to measure electrical resistance is the _____.

_____[80]

1. Pressure
2. Electromotive (e.m.f.)
3. Pressure
4. Volts (or voltage)
5. Friction (or resistance)
6. Resistance
7. Rate
8. Free electrons
9. Ampere
10. Ampere, ohm
11. Ohm, ampere, volt

BASIC ELECTRIC CIRCUITS

84. How can an electric current be made to do useful work?

By connecting the energy or power source (such as a generator or battery) through conductors (such as wires) to the load (the equipment doing work).

85. What name is given to any connected system consisting of a power source, conductors, and load?

An electric circuit.

86. Show a simple electric circuit in a diagram.

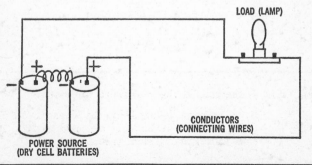

LOAD (LAMP)

CONDUCTORS
(CONNECTING WIRES)

POWER SOURCE
(DRY CELL BATTERIES)

44

87. **In the circuit shown in the preceding frame, what action takes place in terms of electron flow?**

Electrons piling up on the negative pole of the battery cause an electron flow through the electric lamp and back to the battery at the positive pole. The activity of the electron flow through the highly resistant filament of the lamp causes the filament to heat up and glow.

88. **In this circuit, what is the load?**

The lamp.

89. **Does the load offer resistance to the flow of current in the circuit?**

Yes, just as a water wheel or turbine offers resistance to a stream of water.

90. **How do we measure electric resistance?**

In ohms.

91. **In a circuit diagram, what symbol is used for a resistance?**

A saw-toothed figure, like this:

92. **How is the size of the resistance indicated?**

By a numeral followed by the Greek letter Ω (omega). Thus, 10 ohms is indicated as 10Ω, 15 ohms as 15Ω, and 50 ohms as 50Ω.

93. How is a battery indicated in a circuit diagram?

By a combination of long, thin and short, heavy vertical lines, thus:

The short, heavy lines represent the negative poles of individual battery cells; the long, thin lines represent the positive poles.

---

94. In the following symbol, which line represents the positive pole?

The long, thin line.

---

95. In a diagram of a circuit whose power source is a battery, how is the amount of voltage usually indicated?

By a numeral indicating the number of volts, followed by the symbol v. (for volts) written close to the diagram symbol for batteries (or other voltage source, such as a power line).

Example:

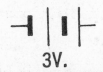

3V.

96. Using only symbols (not pictures) draw a circuit diagram to represent a load (such as a lamp) having a resistance of 2 ohms connected to a 3 volt power source (batteries). Use arrows to show direction of electron flow.

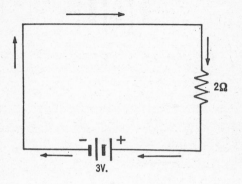

97. Now draw another diagram showing two loads, each having a resistance of 2 ohms, in a circuit with the same power source.

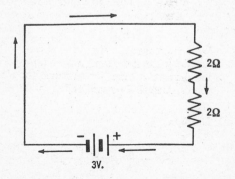

1. An electric current can be made to do useful work when the energy or power source, such as a battery or generator, is connected by means of wires (or other conductors) to the _____.

_____[84]

2. A completely connected system consisting of a power source, conductors, and _____ is called an electric _____.

_____[85]

3. In the circuit diagram shown below (if we disregard the resistance of the wires) the _____ is the electric lamp.

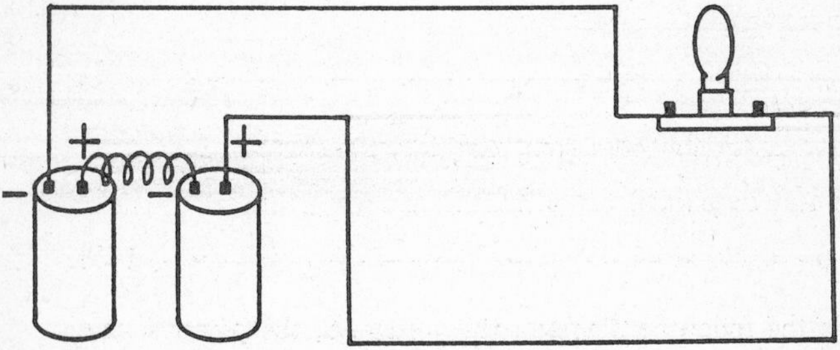

_____[86]

4. In an electric circuit whose power source is a battery, electrons flow from the negative terminal of the battery through the load, and return to the battery at the _____ terminal.

_____[87]

5. Any circuit load offers _____ to the flow of current, just as a water wheel or turbine offers _____ to the flow of water directed against it.

_____ [89]

6. We measure resistance to the flow of current in _____.

_____ [90]

7. In a diagram of an electric circuit, the symbol $-\text{/\/\/\/}-$ is commonly used to indicate _____.

_____ [91]

8. Often the symbol for _____ is accompanied by a numeral followed by Ω, the capital Greek letter omega. In such cases, the numeral tells us the value of the _____, in _____.

_____ [92]

9. The symbol $-|\text{I}|\text{I}|-$ is used in a circuit diagram to indicate a _____.

_____ [93]

0. In this symbol, the long, thin line denotes 2 _____ poles (terminals) of the _____.

_____ [94]

1. In the following diagram, the voltage of the power source is _____ and the resistance of the load is _____.

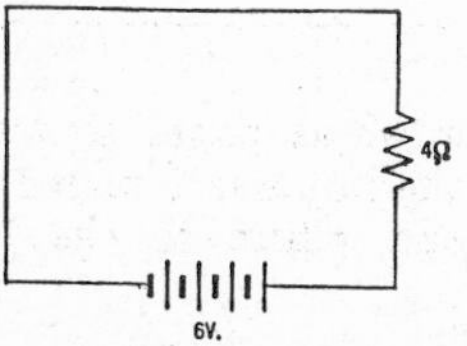

_____ [96]

49

1. Load
2. Load, circuit
3. Load
4. Positive
5. Resistance, resistance
6. Ohms
7. Resistance
8. Resistance, resistance, ohms
9. Battery
10. Positive, battery
11. 6 volts, 4 ohms

OHM'S LAW

98. Do all conductors of electric current have the same resistance?

No. Some materials are better conductors (that is, have less resistance) than others. Moreover, the resistance of every conductor (such as a wire) increases with its length and decreases in an inverse ratio to its cross section. Resistance is also affected by temperature; in general, the higher the temperature of a conductor, the greater its resistance.

99. Can an ohm be defined in terms of the resistance offered by some definite or specific conductor?

Yes. The ohm is, by international agreement, defined as the resistance which a column of mercury of definite, specific cross-section, with a definite length (106.3 centimeters), and a given mass (14.45 grams), offers at a temperature of 0° C.

100. Define an ampere.

An ampere is the rate of flow of current through a resistance of one ohm when the electromotive force is one volt.

01. What law shows the relationship between volts, amperes, and resistance (in ohms)?

Ohm's Law.

02. What is Ohm's Law?

In an electric circuit, the voltage in the circuit is equal to the resistance (in ohms) multiplied by the amperes.

03. Why is Ohm's Law important?

Because it tells us:
1. What voltage is required to operate a circuit—if we know the circuit's resistance and amperage.
2. What the resistance of a circuit is (or may be required) in a circuit—if it is to operate at a given voltage and amperage.
3. How many amperes a circuit will draw—if it has a given resistance and is to operate at a given voltage.

04. Now state Ohm's Law in symbols.

$E = IR$

where E = electromotive force, in volts,
  I = intensity of the current, in amperes,
  R = resistance, in ohms.

05. Using the formula $E = IR$, how can we find the value of I?

If $E = IR$, then $I = \dfrac{E}{R}$

106. **Find what R is equal to, using the formula** $E = IR$.

$$\text{If } E = IR, \quad \text{then} \quad R = \frac{E}{I}$$

107. **In the last few frames we've had a pretty big dose of formulas. Isn't there an easy way to show all the forms of Ohm's Law?**

Yes. When you have a problem involving volts, amperes, and resistance, draw a "pie" and divide it into three pieces—as shown below. Label each part as in the figure. Then, cover the part you want to know. What's left is the formula you need.

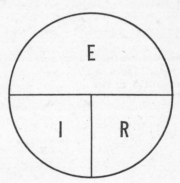

For example:

If you want to know current, cover I:

$$< \frac{E}{R} \text{ remains, and } I = \frac{E}{R} >$$

If you want to know the voltage, cover E:

$$< IR \text{ remains, and } E = IR >$$

If you want to know resistance, cover R:

$$< \frac{E}{I} \text{ remains, and } R = \frac{E}{I} >$$

108. Now, applying Ohm's Law, find out how many volts will be required to light a lamp that draws 1 ampere of current and has a resistance of 2 ohms.

$$E = IR$$
$$= 1 \times 2 = 2$$

2 volts   Ans.

109. How many volts will be required to operate a lamp that draws 2 amperes and has a resistance of 3 ohms?

$$E = 2 \times 3 = 6$$

6 volts   Ans.

110. An appliance having a resistance of 10 ohms is to be operated from a 120 volt line. How many amperes will it draw?

$$I = \frac{E}{R}$$
$$= \frac{120}{10} = 12$$

12 amperes   Ans.

111. An automobile radio draws a current of 2 amperes from a 12 volt battery. What is its resistance?

$$R = \frac{E}{I}$$
$$= \frac{12}{2} = 6$$

6 ohms   Ans.

112. We have seen that Ohm's Law tells us that the voltage in any circuit is equal to the amperage in the circuit multiplied by the resistance ($E = IR$); similarly, that the amperage (I) is equal to the voltage divided by the resistance ($I = \dfrac{E}{R}$). Using these facts, calculate the amperage in a circuit powered by a 3 volt battery and having a load whose resistance is 2 ohms.

$$I = \frac{E}{R} = \frac{3}{2} = 1.5$$

1.5 amperes   Ans.

113. Calculate the amperage if the battery voltage remains the same (3 volts), but the load resistance is 4 ohms.

$$I = \frac{E}{R} = \frac{3}{4} = 0.75$$

0.75 amperes   Ans.

1. Some conductors have more (or less) _____ than others.

   _____[98]

2. The ohm can be defined in terms of the _____ of a column of mercury of specified dimensions.

   _____[99]

3. An ampere is defined as the rate of flow of current through a resistance of one _____ when the electromotive force is one _____.

   _____[100]

4. Ohm's Law defines the relations, in any circuit, of

   _____, _____, and _____.

   _____[101]

5. Ohm's Law states that in an electric circuit, the _____ is always equal to the _____ multiplied by the resistance.

   _____[102]

6. Ohm's Law is important because it tells us how to compute any one of these components if we know the other

   _____.

   _____[103]

7. The equation stating Ohm's Law is __ = IR.

   _____[104]

8. Complete the following equations:

$$I = \frac{E}{-}$$

$$R = \frac{E}{-}$$

_____[105]

9. Ohm's Law tells us that $E = IR$; applying this, find the voltage in a circuit whose current (I) is 2 amperes and whose resistance (R) is 2 ohms.

_____[108]

10. Using the form of Ohm's Law which tells us how the amperage in a circuit can be found if we know voltage and resistance, we learn that an appliance having a resistance of 20 ohms will draw _____ amperes when operated on a 120 volt line.

_____[110]

11. To find the resistance in a circuit when the voltage and amperage are known, we divide the _____ by the

_____.

_____[111]

12. A circuit powered by a 6 volt battery has a load whose resistance is 2 ohms. Using the formula $I = \frac{E}{R}$, we find that the current consumed is _____ amperes.

_____[113]

114. If two or more battery cells are connected together as shown in the diagrams below (in a simple chain formation), how are they said to be connected?

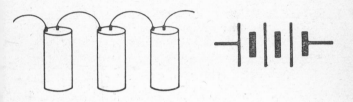

In series.

115. If two or more resistors are connected together thus —\/\/\/\/\/\—\/\/\/\/\/\— (as shown in the last diagram), how are they said to be connected?

In series.

116. If two resistors are connected in series, the current must flow through the first resistor before entering the second; therefore, if two or more resistors are connected in series, what is their total resistance?

The sum of the resistances.

1. Resistance
2. Resistance
3. Ohm, volt
4. Volts, amperes, resistance (in ohms)
5. Voltage, amperage
6. Two

7. E
8. R, I
9. 4 volts
10. 6
11. Voltage, amperage
12. 3

---

117. **In the last diagram (Frame 115), a 2 ohm resistance is in series with another 2 ohm resistance. What is the total resistance?**

   4 ohms.

---

118. **What is the combined resistance of a 2 ohm resistor, 3 ohm resistor, and 4 ohm resistor connected in series?**

   $2 + 3 + 4 = 9$

   9 ohms   Ans.

---

119. **We have seen that Ohm's Law indicates that in any circuit, the amperage is equal to the voltage divided by the resistance ($I = \dfrac{E}{R}$). Using this fact, calculate the amperage in the circuit shown below.**

   $$I = \frac{E}{R} = \frac{3}{9} = 0.333$$

   0.333 amperes   Ans.

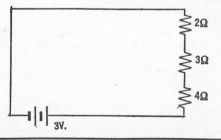

120. A vacuum tube filament has a resistance of 12 ohms. How much current does it consume (how many amperes?) when connected to a 6 volt battery?

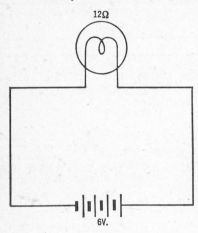

$$I = \frac{E}{R} = \frac{6}{12} = 0.5$$

0.5 amperes   Ans.

121. Ohm's Law tells us that the voltage in a circuit is always the product of the amperage and the resistance amperage (E = IR). Using this fact, find the voltage required to operate a motor when its resistance is 0.04 ohm and draws 150 amperes.

$$E = IR = 150 \times 0.04 = 6$$

6 volts   Ans.

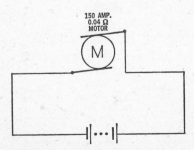

1. Two or more batteries are said to be connected in

   _____ when they are connected in a chain formation, with the positive terminal of one wired to the
   negative of the next.

   _____[114]

2. Two or more resistors are said to be connected in

   _____ if they are wired together in a chain formation, one after another.

   _____[115]

3. The combined (or total) resistance of several resistances
   connected in this way (as described in the previous ques-

   tion) is simply the _____ of the resistances.

   _____[116]

4. If each of two resistances so connected has a resistance of

   3 ohms, their combined resistance is _____ ohms.

   _____[117]

5. A series of three resistors has a total resistance of 10
   ohms if the first resistor has a resistance of 5 ohms, the

   second 3 ohms, and the third _____ ohms.

   _____[118]

6. In the following circuit, the total resistance is _____ ohms.

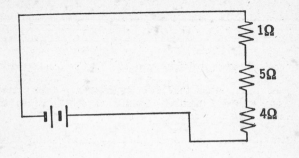

_____[119]

1. Series
2. Series
3. Sum
4. 6
5. 2
6. 10

RESISTANCES IN PARALLEL

122. When resistances are connected together like links in a chain, they are said to be connected in series. What name is given to the connection of resistances parallel to each other, like this?

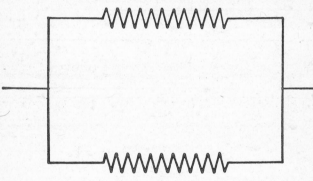

Parallel.

123. If a circuit contains resistors connected in parallel, what is the effect on the flow of free electrons in the circuit?

The free electrons are given more than one path through which to flow.

124. Does this mean that the rate of flow of electric current (that is, amperage) is greater when there are two or more paths than when there is only one?

Yes, just as two or more pipes leading separately from a tank will empty the tank more rapidly (that is, offer less resistance to the flow) than a single pipe (of no larger diameter).

125. Show this effect with another example.

If a five-lane highway empties into a two-lane bridge, the bridge will offer a measurable resistance to the flow of traffic. There would be less resistance if there were two such bridges parallel to each other, providing alternate routes for the traffic. There would be still less resistance if there were additional bridges.

126. How can we calculate the total resistance of two or more resistances connected in parallel?

By the formula:

$$\frac{1}{R_t} = \frac{1}{R_1} + \frac{1}{R_2} + \frac{1}{R_3}$$

where R_t = total resistance,
R_1 = one resistor,
R_2 = a second resistor,
R_3 = a third resistor, etc.

127. State this law in words.

If two or more resistances are connected in parallel, the reciprocal of the total resistance is equal to the sum of reciprocals of the individual resistances.

128. What is the reciprocal of a number?

The number 1 divided by the given number. Thus, the reciprocal of 2 is $\frac{1}{2}$; of 3, $\frac{1}{3}$; of 7, $\frac{1}{7}$.

129. What is the easiest way of finding the reciprocal of a fraction?

By inverting the fraction. Thus, the reciprocal of $\frac{1}{3}$ is $\frac{3}{1}$, or 3; the reciprocal of $\frac{2}{3}$ is $\frac{3}{2}$; the reciprocal of $\frac{3}{4}$ is $\frac{4}{3}$.

(NOTE: In engineering operations, it is usually most convenient to work with fractional quantities when they are expressed in decimal form.)

130. Find the combined resistance of a 2 ohm and 3 ohm resistor connected in parallel.

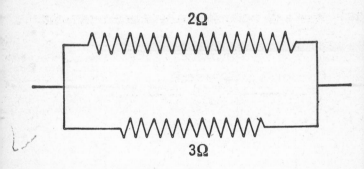

$$\frac{1}{R_t} = \frac{1}{R_1} + \frac{1}{R_2}$$
$$\frac{1}{R_t} = \frac{1}{2} + \frac{1}{3} = \frac{5}{6}$$
$$\therefore R_t = \frac{6}{5} = 1.2$$

1.2 ohms   Ans.

131. Three resistors, each having a value of 2 ohms, are connected in parallel. What is the total resistance?

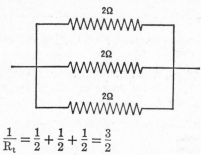

$$\frac{1}{R_t} = \frac{1}{2} + \frac{1}{2} + \frac{1}{2} = \frac{3}{2}$$

$$\therefore R_t = \frac{2}{3} = 0.666$$

0.666 ohms   Ans.

132. What is the total resistance in the circuit indicated below?

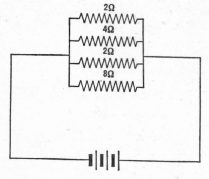

$$\frac{1}{R_t} = \frac{1}{2} + \frac{1}{4} + \frac{1}{2} + \frac{1}{8} = \frac{11}{8}$$

$$\therefore R_t = \frac{8}{11} = 0.727$$

0.727 ohms   Ans.

133. If the power source in the circuit shown in the preceding frame is a 12 volt battery, how many amperes flow through the circuit?

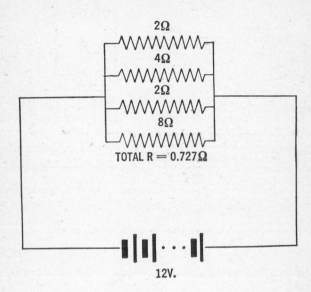

$$I = \frac{E}{R} = \frac{12}{0.727} = 16.5$$

16.5 amperes   Ans.

---

134. How is the total resistance in a circuit found when the circuit contains both resistors in series and resistors in parallel?

The resistors in parallel are first converted to a total resistance (for each group, if there is more than one); this total is then added to the sum of resistors in series.

35. Calculate the total resistance in the following circuit.

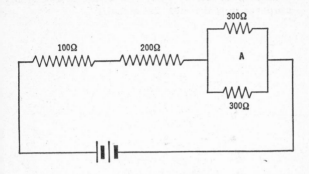

$$(1) \quad \frac{1}{R_{\text{Ⓐ}}} = \frac{1}{300} + \frac{1}{300} = \frac{2}{300}$$

$$R_{\text{Ⓐ}} = \frac{300}{2} = 150\Omega$$

(2) Total R $= (100 + 200) + 150 = 450$

450 ohms   Ans.

36. What voltage is required to maintain a current of one ampere in the circuit shown in the preceding frame?

$$E = IR$$
$$= 1 \times 450 = 450$$

450 volts   Ans.

37. What is the general rule for computing the total resistance in a circuit which has resistors both in series and in parallel?

Find the total resistance of the resistors in parallel . . . then add this to the sum of the resistors in series.

1. When resistances are placed in a circuit in such a way that all of the terminals at one end of the resistances are connected together and all the terminals at the other end of the resistances are connected together, the resistances are said to be connected in _____.

_____[122]

2. Resistors so connected provide more than one path through which the _____ can flow.

_____[123]

3. As a result, the circuit offers _____ resistance than it would if there were only one path.

_____[124]

4. Similarly, a highway leading to two or more bridges offers _____ resistance to traffic flow than a highway connected to only a single bridge (of the same width and length).

_____[125]

5. $\frac{1}{R_t} = \frac{1}{R_1} + \frac{1}{R_2} + \frac{1}{R_3}$ is a formula which tells us how to compute the _____ resistance of two or more resistances in _____.

_____[126]

6. The reciprocal of a number is _____ divided by that number.

_____[128]

68

7. In practical calculation, to find the reciprocal of a number expressed as a fraction, we simply _____ the fraction. Thus $\frac{1}{3}$ becomes $\frac{3}{1}$, or 3; 3 (that is $\frac{3}{1}$) becomes $\frac{1}{3}$.

———————————————————————————[129]

8. If $\frac{1}{R_t} = \frac{1}{4} + \frac{1}{4} + \frac{1}{4}$ ohms, then R_t is the reciprocal of

$\frac{3}{4}$, or _____ ohms.

———————————————————————————[130]

9. If a circuit contains both resistors in series and resistors in parallel, we find the total resistance of the circuit by converting each group of resistances in parallel to an equivalent resistance for that group, then adding these to

the sum of the other resistances in _____.

———————————————————————————[134, 137]

1. Parallel
2. Free electrons (or current)
3. Less
4. Less
5. Total, parallel
6. 1
7. Invert
8. $\frac{4}{3}$ (or 1.333)
9. Series

ELECTRIC POWER

138. What is power (in physics)?

The rate of doing work. (In other words, the amount of work done divided by the time required to do it.)

139. What is the common unit of power used in electric engineering?

The watt.

140. How is a watt defined?

One watt is equal to one volt at the rate of one ampere.

141. How do we compute the wattage of a circuit?

We multiply the voltage by the current (in amperes.)

142. State this fact in the form of a formula.

$$P = EI$$

When P = power (in watts),
     E = electromotive force (in volts),
     I = rate of current flow (in amperes).

---

143. An electric light bulb operating on a 12 volt battery consumes 2 amperes of current. What is its power rating in watts?

$$P = EI$$
$$= 12 \times 2 = 24$$

               24 watts   Ans.

---

144. How many watts of power are delivered by a 120 volt appliance drawing 3 amperes?

$$P = EI$$
$$= 120 \times 3 = 360$$

               360 watts   Ans.

---

145. Are there other ways of writing the formula P = EI?

Yes. If P = EI, it follows that

$$E = \frac{P}{I}, \text{ and}$$

$$I = \frac{P}{E}.$$

146. **Isn't there some easy way to diagram all the forms of the power formulas?**

Yes. We can use the same kind of a "pie" diagram that we used for Ohm's Law. (Turn back to Frame 107.) In this case, we simply put P in the upper slice, E and I in each of the lower slices. Cover the part you want to know. What is left is the formula you need.

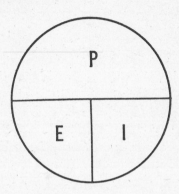

If you want to know current, cover I:
$$< \frac{P}{E} \text{ remains, and } I = \frac{P}{E} >$$

If you want to know the wattage, cover P:
$$< EI \text{ remains, and } P = EI >$$

If you want to know the voltage, cover E:
$$< \frac{P}{I} \text{ remains, and } E = \frac{P}{I} >$$

---

147. **Using one of the forms of the power formula, find the number of amperes used by a 60 watt lamp operating on a 120 volt line.**

$$I = \frac{P}{E} = \frac{60}{120} = 0.5$$

0.5 amperes   Ans.

---

148. Using the formula $E = \dfrac{P}{I}$, determine how many volts will be required to operate a 60 watt lamp that draws 2 amperes.

$$E = \frac{P}{I} = \frac{60}{2} = 30$$

30 volts   Ans.

1. In physics, _____ is defined as the rate of doing work.

_____[138]

2. The watt is the common unit of _____ used in _____ engineering.

_____[139]

3. The watt can be defined as the work done by an electromotive force of one _____ at the current rate of one _____.

_____[140]

4. To compute the wattage of a power circuit we merely multiply the _____ by the amperage.

_____[141]

5. P = EI is the formula for _____.

_____[142]

6. In the formula P = EI, P stands for _____ (in _____).

_____[142]

7. In the formula P = EI, E stands for electromotive force (in _____), and I for rate of current flow (in _____).

_____[142]

8. An electric light bulb operating on a 12 volt battery and consuming 3 amperes of current has a power rating of _____ watts.

_____[143]

9. The power rating of a 120 volt appliance drawing 2 amperes of current is _____ watts.

_____[144]

10. The formula $P = EI$ can also be written as $E = \frac{?}{?}$, and $I = \frac{?}{?}$.

_____[145]

11. If the current consumed by an electric appliance is equal to the power (in watts) divided by the voltage, it follows that a 240 watt iron operating on a 120 volt line will draw _____ amperes of current.

_____[147]

12. If we know the power rating of an appliance (in watts) and the number of amperes it draws, we can find the voltage required to operate it by dividing the _____ by the _____.

_____[148]

1. Power
2. Power, electric
3. Volt, ampere
4. Voltage
5. Electric power (in watts)
6. Electric power, watts
7. Volts, amperes

8. 36
9. 240
10. $\dfrac{P}{I}, \dfrac{P}{E}$
11. 2
12. Power rating (in watts), amperage

FUSES AND POWER LOADS

149. Do all electric conductors, such as wires, have resistance?

Yes.

150. How does a resistance behave when current is passed through it?

It generates heat because of "friction" with the moving electrons. (Rub your hands together.)

151. What happens when a relatively heavy power load is carried by house wiring?

The wires tend to become hot. The smaller the cross-section of the wire, the greater the resistance of the wire, hence the hotter the wire becomes. (For this reason heavy wires—wires of relatively great thickness—are required in circuits carrying heavy power loads, such as large air conditioners, electric heaters, and broilers.)

152. If a circuit, not protected by any safety device, carries a load too heavy for the wires to carry safely, what danger can be expected?

The wires may heat to the point where they set fire to the structure in which they have been placed. The heat can also burn off the protective insulation surrounding the wires, creating other hazards.

153. What is the most common protective device used to prevent overloading of a circuit?

A fuse.

154. What is a fuse?

A cartridge or capsule containing a piece of wire with a relatively low melting point. When such a device is connected in series with the load, the wire in the fuse will melt if the current flowing through it is greater than its capacity. When the fuse wire melts, the circuit is broken.

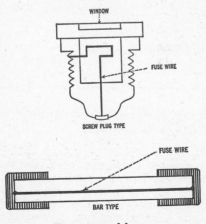

Two types of fuses.

155. How are fuses marked?

In terms of the number of amperes they will carry. A 10 ampere fuse will carry up to 10 amperes of current before melting, a 20 ampere fuse up to 20 amperes, etc.

156. What size fuse is necessary to carry a load consisting of five 100 watt light bulbs and a 1000 watt electric broiler in series . . . on a standard 120 volt line?

The combined load is 1500 watts. The formula $I = \dfrac{P}{E}$ tells us that the amperage consumed is equal to the wattage divided by the voltage, or $\frac{1500}{120} = 12.5$ amperes. A 15 ampere fuse should be adequate.

157. What is a convenient rule of thumb to use in calculating the load that can be carried on a standard 110-120 volt house line without blowing a fuse?

Assume that each 100 watts of power used will draw approximately 1 ampere of current. Thus, a 15 ampere fuse will carry a load of up to 1500 watts, a 20 ampere fuse up to 2000 watts.

158. Why is a fuse always connected *in series* with the load and the power source?

Because if it is in series with the load, it will automatically disconnect the load when it melts. (See illustration.)

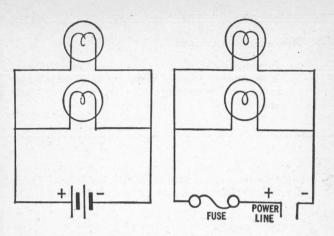

Unprotected and protected circuits.

159. Why is it a dangerous practice to use larger fuses than wiring specifications indicate?

Because this would defeat the purpose of a fuse—which is to prevent overloading of the circuit. Building codes specify the safe current-carrying values of every kind of house-wiring. The size of fuse to be used is determined by this limit—not by power requirements of the load.

160. Are fuses used for other purposes than the prevention of overheating in power lines?

Yes. Fuses are often used to protect appliances from damage, should some accident occur to the equipment or to the connecting lines. Suppose a machine driven by an electric motor should jam; if a fuse of proper size were in series with the line, the fuse would "blow" before the equipment was damaged.

161. What is a kilowatt?

1000 watts.

---

162. How many 100 watt lamps can be lighted by a generator which has an output of one kilowatt?

10

---

163. The watt is a common unit of power used in electric engineering. What unit of power is generally used in describing the work capacity of gasoline engines and electric motors?

The horsepower.

---

164. Is there a relationship between watts and horsepower?

Yes. Approximately 746 watts = 1 horsepower.

---

165. What is the rating in watts of an electric motor that delivers 2 horsepower (assuming 100% efficiency)?

$2 \times 746 = 1492$ watts.

---

166. What formula shows the relation of amperage to watts?

$$I = \frac{P}{E}$$

---

167. Use this formula to find the number of amperes drawn by a 1 horsepower (746 watts) electric motor operating on a 115 volt line.

$$I = \frac{P}{E} = \frac{746}{115} = 6.48$$

6.48 amperes   Ans.

1. All electric conductors have resistance; therefore, when a current is passed through them, they generate _____.

   _____[150]

2. In general, the smaller the diameter a wire has, the more resistance it offers, hence the more _____ it generates relative to the power it carries. For this reason, heavy loads require relatively _____ wires to minimize fire hazards.

   _____[151]

3. A fuse is a common protective device used to prevent the _____ of a circuit.

   _____[153]

4. A fuse is essentially a small piece of wire that _____ when more than a predetermined amount of current passes through it. If such a wire is connected in _____ with the load, it will break the circuit (disconnect the load) when the current-carrying capacity of the fuse is exceeded.

   _____[154]

5. Fuses are marked in terms of the number of _____ they will carry.

   _____[155]

6. A convenient rule of thumb to use in calculating amperage consumed by loads on a standard 110-120 volt power line is that each _____ watts draws approximately _____ ampere of current.

   _____[157]

7. A load of 1000 watts, at 110-120 volts, can be carried by a _____ ampere fuse.

   _____[157]

8. To calculate exactly the current consumption (in amperes) of a power load, we simply _____ the wattage by the voltage.

_____[156]

9. We can estimate roughly the load that can be carried by a fuse (used on a standard 110-120 volt house line) by assuming that each 100 watts of load will draw _____ of current. Thus, a 15 _____ fuse will carry up to _____ watts without melting (blowing).

_____[157]

10. It is a dangerous practice to use a fuse larger than that specified for certain application, because the use of too large a fuse would defeat its purpose, which is to prevent _____ a circuit.

_____[159]

11. Fuses are also used to protect equipment from _____, should an accident occur in the equipment, or if excessive voltage should be applied to the line.

_____[160]

12. The unit of power which represents 1000 watts is called a _____.

_____[161]

13. Ten 100 watt lamps can be lighted by a generator which has an output of one _____.

_____[162]

14. If we want to describe the work capacity of an electric motor, we can translate the rating of the motor in watts into units of _____, assuming that approximately 746 watts is the equivalent of one _____ (assuming 100% efficiency).

_____[164]

1. Heat
2. Heat, large
3. Overloading
4. Melts, series
5. Amperes
6. 100, 1
7. 10

8. Divide
9. One ampere, ampere, 1500
10. Overloading
11. Damage
12. Kilowatt
13. Kilowatt
14. Horsepower, horsepower

GENERATING ELECTRIC CURRENT

168. What are the most common means of generating an electric current?

1. Batteries, either dry cells or storage batteries.
2. Magnetos or generators, which rotate a conductor across the lines of force of a magnetic field.

169. How does a battery or cell operate?

If two different metals, or carbon and a metal, are immersed in a solution that produces a greater chemical action on one than on the other, the substance affected by the greater chemical action acquires an excess of free electrons—with respect to the other. If the two substances are then joined by a conductor (such as a wire), the excess free electrons accumulated by one (where the chemical action is greater) will flow through the conductor to the other. This flow of free electrons is an electric current.

170. What do we call the two metals (or metal and carbon) which, when immersed in a suitably active solution, form the cell of a battery?

Electrodes.

171. Which electrode has the greater number of free electrons?

The negative electrode.

172. What is the direction of electron flow (current) in a circuit connected to a battery?

From negative to positive (minus to plus).

173. What substances are used for the electrodes of an ordinary flashlight battery (the cheapest and most familiar cell)?

Carbon and zinc.

174. Which electrode is in the center of the ordinary flashlight battery or dry cell?

The carbon electrode, which is the positive electrode.

175. Which electrode of a flashlight battery cell is the negative electrode?

The zinc, which is usually the casing of the cell.

176. Is there a distinction between the meanings usually attached to the words "cell" and "battery"?

Technically, a battery is a collection of cells connected together (usually in series). In ordinary usage, however, any cell is called a battery.

177. What is meant by connecting cells in series?

Connecting the positive electrode of each cell to the negative electrode of the next . . . and so on . . . to the end of the line. The connections are shown in the illustrations below.

178. What is the total voltage produced by a number of cells connected in series?

The sum of the voltage of the individual cells.

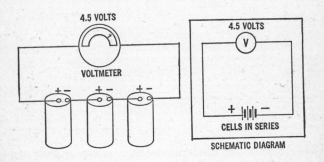

Connection of cells in series.

179. What is the total amperage of a number of cells connected in series?

The amperage of a single cell.

180. Cells are sometimes connected in parallel. Why?

To provide more amperage than a single cell can supply. Thus, cells in parallel can keep a piece of electric equipment (such as a lamp or signal beacon) operating for a longer time than a single cell could; also (as will be seen in the section on power), some equipment, operating at a fixed voltage, requires more amperage than could be supplied by a single cell.

181. How are cells connected in parallel?

All the negative electrodes are connected together and all the positive electrodes are connected together, as in the following diagram.

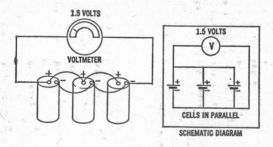

Connection of cells in parallel.

182. What is the total voltage of a group of cells connected in parallel?

The voltage of a single cell.

183. What is the voltage output of six 1.5 volt cells connected in parallel?

1.5 volts.

184. What is the amperage of a group of cells connected in parallel?

The sum of the amperage of the individual cells.

185. What are magnetos and generators?

Devices that generate an electric current (flow of electrons in a coil of wire) by rotating the coil through a magnetic field.

186. How does the motion of a coil in a magnetic field create a flow of electrons within the coil?

To answer this, it is first necessary to explain the nature of magnets and magnetic fields. This is the subject of the following section.

1. Batteries and generators (or magnetos) are the most commonly used power sources to provide for _____.

   _____[168]

2. If two different metals, or if carbon and a metal, are immersed in a solution that produces a greater chemical action on one than another, the resulting action can release _____ which can flow, along a conductor, from one of the substances to the other. This flow of _____ is an electric current.

   _____[169]

3. The two metals, or metal and carbon, which are immersed in the solution (or paste) of a battery cell are called _____.

   _____[170]

4. In a battery, the _____ which contains the greater number of free _____ is called the negative _____.

   _____[171]

5. The direction of electron flow in a circuit connected to a battery is from the _____ electrode to the _____ electrode.

   _____[172]

6. Carbon and _____ are the substances that are used for _____ in an ordinary flashlight battery.

   _____[173]

7. In the ordinary flashlight battery, the _____ electrode, which is the positive electrode, is in the _____ of the cell.

_____[174]

8. The negative electrode of an ordinary flashlight battery is made of _____ and forms the _____ of the battery.

_____[175]

9. In strict usage, a battery refers to a collection of _____; it is customary today, however, to refer to any _____ as a "battery."

_____[176]

10. When the positive electrode of one cell is connected to the negative electrode of another, and the positive electrode of the second connected to the negative electrode of a third, the cells are said to be connected in _____.

_____[177]

11. If cells are connected in the manner indicated above, the total voltage available is the _____ of the voltage of the individual cells.

_____[178]

12. To make more amperage available in a circuit, battery cells are sometimes connected in _____.

_____[180]

13. If a number of batteries are connected in such a way that all the negative electrodes are connected together, and all the positive electrodes together, the cells are said to be connected in _____.

_____[181]

90

14. If a group of cells is connected in parallel, the total voltage of the group is no greater than _____.

_____[182]

15. If 14 cells, each of 1.5 volts, are connected in parallel, the total voltage of the group is _____.

_____[183]

16. Magnetos and electric generators are devices that create an electric current as a result of the rotation of a _____ through a _____ field.

_____[185]

✓ ANSWERS: SPOT CHECK 12

1. Electric current (or electricity)
2. Free electrons, free electrons
3. Electrodes
4. Electrode, electrons, electrode
5. Negative, positive
6. Zinc, electrodes
7. Carbon, center
8. Zinc, casing
9. Cells, cell
10. Series
11. Sum
12. Parallel
13. Parallel
14. The voltage of a single cell
15. 1.5
16. Coil, magnetic

MAGNETISM AND ELECTROMAGNETISM

BAR MAGNETS

187. What is a magnet?

An object that attracts iron and steel and which, if free to rotate, will move to a fixed position relative to (or pointing toward) the north pole.

188. Can magnets attract material other than iron and steel?

Yes. Some materials, such as nickel and cobalt, are also affected by magnetic attraction—but to a lesser extent.

189. What is a magnetic field?

The region around a magnet in which its force can be measured.

190. What is a permanent magnet?

A magnet (usually of steel, or an alloy containing steel) which maintains a permanent field (as compared with an electromagnet, which has a magnetic field only when an electric current is flowing through it).

191. How are permanent magnets made?

Usually by placing a piece of steel (or some alloy with similar properties) momentarily within a strong magnetic field. Rubbing such a metal with another magnet also magnetizes the metal.

192. What is a bar magnet?

A permanent magnet in the shape of a bar.

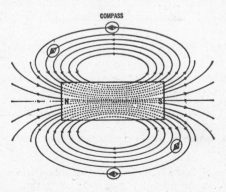

Magnetic field around a bar magnet.

193. What is a horseshoe magnet?

A permanent magnet in the shape of a horseshoe.

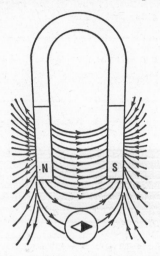

Magnetic field around a horseshoe magnet.

---

194. If a bar magnet is dipped into iron filings, how will filings arrange themselves around the magnet?

A large number of filings will cling to the magnet at both ends, but few will attach themselves to the magnet near its center.

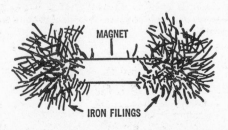

---

195. Why do more filings cling to the ends than to the middle of the magnet?

The attraction (force) of the magnet is concentrated at the two ends.

---

196. What is the needle of a compass?

A small bar magnet, free to rotate.

---

197. If a magnet is free to rotate, what action can we expect?

The magnet will turn to a north-south direction.

---

198. What can we learn about the earth from the fact that a compass needle always tends to line up in a north-south direction?

That the earth itself is a bar magnet.

---

199. What name is given to the two ends of a magnet?

Poles. The pole of the magnet which (when the magnet is free to rotate) always turns toward the north is called the north-seeking pole, or north pole; the other is called the south-seeking pole, or south pole.

---

200. If the north pole of one magnet is brought close to the south pole of another magnet, what will happen?

The two poles will attract each other.

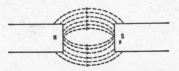

201. If the north pole of one magnet is brought close to the north pole of another magnet, what will happen?

The two poles will repel each other.

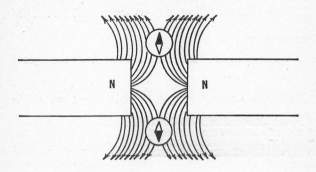

Magnetic field between like poles.

202. State the basic law of magnetism that is illustrated in Frames 200 and 201.

Unlike poles attract each other, and like poles repel each other.

1. A magnet has the property of attracting _____ and

   _____.

   _____[187]

2. The region around a magnet in which the force of the
   magnet is effective is called a magnetic _____.

   _____[189]

3. A magnet that maintains a permanent magnetic field
   around it is called a _____.

   _____[190]

4. Magnets of this type are usually made by placing, momentarily, a piece of steel, or some other alloy of iron, inside

   a strong _____.

   _____[191]

5. A bar magnet is a _____ magnet in the shape of a
   bar.

   _____[192]

6. The same type of magnet shaped as a horseshoe is called

   a _____.

   _____[193]

7. If a bar magnet is dipped into iron filings, many filings will cling to the magnet at its poles, but few at its

_____.

_____[194]

8. This fact indicates that the attractive force of a bar magnet is concentrated at the magnet's _____.

_____[195]

9. The needle of a magnetic compass is simply a _____ magnet left free to rotate.

_____[196]

10. A magnetized rod (free to rotate) will always tend to swing to a position in which one end points _____, the other _____.

_____[197]

11. The behavior of a magnetic compass needle indicates that the earth itself is a _____.

_____[198]

12. The ends of a bar magnet are called the _____ of the magnet.

_____[199]

13. The north pole of one magnet will attract the _____ of another magnet.

_____[200]

14. Unlike magnetic poles _____ each other, and _____ poles repel each other.

_____[202]

1. Iron, steel
2. Field
3. Permanent magnet
4. Magnetic field
5. Permanent
6. Horseshoe magnet
7. Center
8. Ends
9. Bar
10. North, south (or south, north)
11. Bar magnet
12. Poles
13. South
14. Attract, like

MAGNETIC FORCE

203. **What is a magnetic field?**

The region around a magnet in which its force (attractive or repulsive) can be measured.

204. **Around what part of a magnet is the magnetic field concentrated?**

Around the poles.

205. **What unit is commonly used to measure the force (attraction or repulsion) exerted by a magnetic field?**

The dyne.

206. **What is a dyne?**

A unit of force; specifically, the amount of force required to cause a mass of 1 gram to accelerate 1 centimeter per second for each second the force acts.

207. How is the dyne used to define a unit of magnetic force?

> The basic magnetic (or electromagnetic) unit, sometimes called the unit pole, is defined as the attractive (or repelling) strength required (in a vacuum) for a pole to exert a force of 1 dyne upon an equal pole 1 centimeter away.

208. How is a magnetic field pictured?

> As a curving bundle of lines of force.

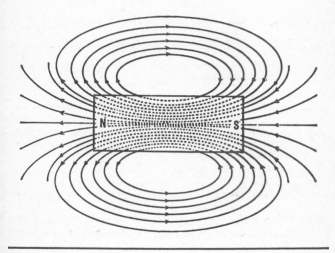

209. What name is given to the total number of lines of force occupying a region of magnetic activity?

> Magnetic flux.

210. What is the unit of magnetic flux?

> The maxwell, which is thought of as one line of magnetic flux.

211. If we want to know the intensity of a magnetic field, what facts do we require?

The number of lines of magnetic flux (that is, the number of maxwells) per unit area, say per square centimeter.

212. What term do we use to refer to the number of persons per square mile?

Population density.

213. What term does this fact suggest for the number of lines of flux (number of maxwells) per square centimeter?

Flux density.

214. Do magnetic lines of force actually exist?

Lines of force are merely a useful concept. There is no experimental evidence that they exist in the way they are pictured.

1. The region around a magnet in which its force (attractive or repulsive) can be measured is called a _____.

   _____[203]

2. The dyne is the unit commonly used to measure the _____ of a magnetic _____.

   _____[205]

3. The dyne can be defined as the amount of _____ required to accelerate a mass of _____ gram, _____ centimeter per second for each second the force acts.

   _____[206]

4. Curving bundles of lines of force are generally used to provide an imaginary picture of a magnetic _____.

   _____[208]

5. The term magnetic flux is used to refer to the total number of lines of force imagined to occupy (cut through) a region of _____ activity (field).

   _____[209]

6. The maxwell is the basic unit used to indicate the relative strength of _____.

   _____[210]

7. The maxwell is regarded as a single line of _____.

   _____[210]

8. To indicate the relative strength of a magnetic field, we state the number of lines of magnetic flux—that is the number of _____—that occupy a unit area.

_____[211]

9. The flux density of a magnetic field is the number of _____ cutting through each square centimeter of that field.

_____[213]

ELECTROMAGNETISM

215. So far we have considered only the relatively permanent magnetic fields around substances that have been magnetized. What name is given to magnetized substances whose fields remain more or less permanent?

Permanent magnets.

216. What other type of magnet plays an important role in electric engineering?

The electromagnet.

217. What is an electromagnet?

A magnet whose field is created by a current in a coil of wire. The field of such a magnet exists only so long as current flows through the coil.

218. On what principle is the electromagnet based?

The Oersted effect.

219. What is the Oersted effect?

The occurrence of a magnetic field around every wire carrying an electric current.

(NOTE: This discovery was made in 1819 by the Danish physicist Hans Christian Oersted [1777-1851].)

1. Magnetic field
2. Force, field
3. Force, 1, 1
4. Field
5. Magnetic

6. Magnetic flux
7. Magnetic flux
8. Maxwells
9. Lines of flux (or maxwells)

220. Describe an experiment that demonstrates the Oersted effect.

Hold a magnetic compass near a wire through which current is flowing. The needle will be deflected. Disconnect the current source from the wire. The needle will return to its initial position.

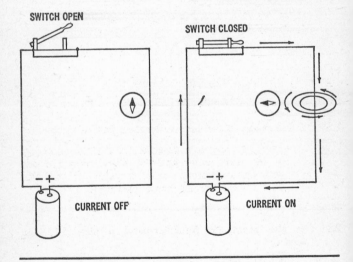

221. How can we find the direction of the magnetic field around a current-carrying conductor?

By using the left-hand rule.

222. What is the left-hand rule?

The rule which makes use of the thumb and fingers of the left hand to determine the direction of the magnetic field around a conductor: Grasp the conductor with the left hand, the thumb extended in the direction of electron flow. The other fingers will then point in the direction of the field.

The left-hand rule.

223. What is the direction of electron flow in a circuit?

From the negative terminal of the power source to the positive terminal—in short, from the side with more electrons (hence, negative) to the side with fewer electrons (hence, positive).

224. Is the magnetic field around a straight wire strong?

No. It is weak.

225. How can we make the field stronger?

By bending the wire to form a loop.

226. Why does a loop of wire have more field strength than a straight wire?

Because in a loop the lines of force are concentrated at the center.

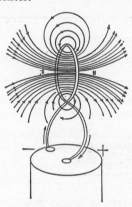

227. If looping a wire concentrates its magnetic field, how would we go about creating a field having a greater intensity than that of a single loop?

We would provide more loops; that is, we would wind a number of turns of wire to form a coil.

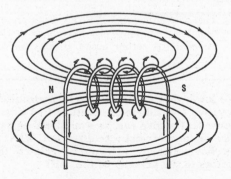

Magnetic field of a coil.

228. How would we find the field strength of a coil?

The field strength of a coil is found by multiplying the field strength of one loop by the number of loops (that is, number of turns).

229. What is a solenoid?

A coil of wire whose length is greater than its radius.

230. When current flows through a solenoid, what effect can we observe?

A magnetic pole at each end of the coil. In short, when current flows through a solenoid, the solenoid becomes a magnet.

231. When current no longer flows through a solenoid, what is the effect?

The coil is no longer magnetic.

232. If a solenoid, when activated, is a magnet, which end is the north pole and which end is the south pole?

The answer depends on the direction of current flow (electron flow), and whether the coil is wound (relative to a certain position) clockwise or counterclockwise.

233. We know that electrons flow in a circuit from the negative (−) side to the positive (+) side. We also know that a wire can be wound either in a clockwise or counterclockwise direction. What rule that we have already considered relates these two factors to the polarity of the coil?

The left-hand rule.

234. How is the left-hand rule applied to determine the polarity of a solenoid?

Grasp the coil in the left hand, with the fingers (other than the thumb) curving in the direction of the electron flow (negative to positive). The thumb will then point to the north pole of the solenoid.

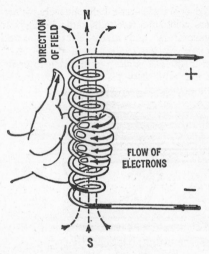

Left-hand rule for coils.

235. How can the strength of a solenoid be increased without adding turns of wire or increasing the current flow?

By inserting a soft iron core in the coil of the solenoid.

236. Why does an iron core increase the strength of the field?

Because the iron itself contributes additional lines of force.

237. What do we call a solenoid which is wound around a soft iron core?

An electromagnet.

238. What are some common uses of electromagnets?

To operate electric bells, buzzers, telegraph sounders, telephone receivers, radio loudspeakers, motors, generators, and many electric measuring instruments, such as voltameters and ammeters. Electromagnets also make the invisible recordings on magnetic tape that play such an important part in modern science and industry.

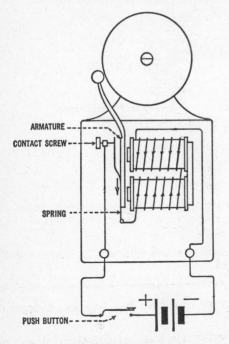

A multiple-stroke electric bell.

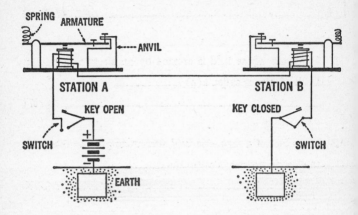

A simple two-way telegraph line. When key is closed at the sending station (Station A in diagram), the electromagnets attract armatures on the sounding devices.

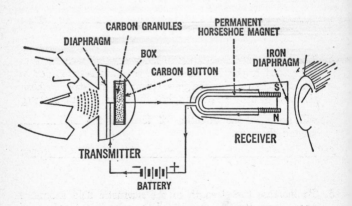

A simple one-way telephone system.

1. A magnet whose field is created by an electric current in a coil of wire is called a(n) _____.

_____[217]

2. The effect of a magnetic field surrounding a wire carrying an electric current is called the _____.

_____[219]

3. The fact that a wire conducting an electric current is surrounded by a _____ is easily demonstrated. All we have to do is move a magnetic compass around the wire; the field surrounding the wire will _____ the compass needle.

_____[220]

4. The left-hand rule tells us that if a current-carrying wire is grasped in the left hand, with the thumb extending in the direction of electron flow (from the negative to positive side of the current supply), the other fingers, curving, will point in the direction of force of the _____ around the wire.

_____[222]

5. To increase the strength of the magnetic field around a wire, all we have to do is bend the wire into the form of a _____.

_____[225]

6. When a straight wire (carrying a current) is formed into a _____, the lines of force (magnetic field) around the wire become concentrated at the _____ of the _____.

_____[226]

7. To increase the field strength of a current-carrying wire still further, we merely increase the number of _____ around a common center.

_____[227]

8. If the length of a wire coil is greater than its radius, the coil is called a _____.

_____[229]

9. When a current flows through such a coil, the coil behaves like a _____.

_____[230]

10. A solenoid ceases to behave like a _____ when no _____ passes through it (that is, when it is disconnected from the power source).

_____[231]

11. Which end of a solenoid becomes a north pole, and which a south pole, depends on the direction of _____ and on the direction of the loops.

_____[234]

12. We can increase the field strength of a solenoid by inserting a _____ in the coil of the solenoid.

_____[235]

114

239. If a bar magnet is thrust into a solenoid (coil of wire) that has no current flowing through it, what occurs in the coil?

An electric current moves through the coil, but ceases as soon as the magnet comes to rest.

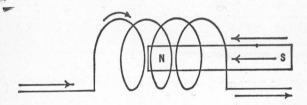

240. What happens in the coil when the magnet is jerked back out of the solenoid?

Again, an electric current is created (as long as the magnetic field is in motion within the solenoid), but this time the current flows in the opposite direction.

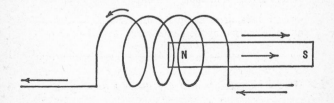

1. Electromagnet
2. Oersted effect
3. Magnetic field, deflect
4. Magnetic field
5. Loop
6. Loop, center, loop
7. Loops
8. Solenoid
9. Magnet
10. Magnet, current
11. Current flow (or electron flow)
12. Soft iron core

241. What two facts are illustrated by these two experiments?

1. That when a conductor (in this case the coil) is cut by (or cuts across) the lines of a magnetic field, a flow of free electrons occurs in the conductor.
2. That the direction of this flow reverses with the direction of the motion of the conductor relative to the magnetic field.

242. Does it make any difference whether the magnet moves relative to the conductor, or the conductor moves relative to the magnet?

No.

243. How could we make use of this effect to generate a continuous electric current?

By rotating a coil continuously between the poles of a magnet (either a permanent magnet or an electromagnet).

244. What is a magneto?

A device for generating an electric current by rotating a coil between the poles of a permanent magnet.

245. What is an electric generator?

A device for generating an electric current by rotating a coil between the poles of an electromagnet.

246. What does a magneto look like?

Like this:

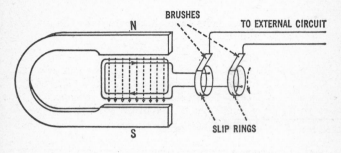

247. What does a generator look like?

Like this:

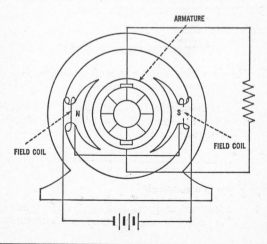

248. **What do we call the revolving coil in a magneto or generator?**

The armature.

---

249. **When a magnet was thrust into a coil, we saw that it produced a flow of current through the coil in one direction; when the magnet was withdrawn, we saw that the current flow was reversed. What conclusion followed?**

That the negative (electron-rich) and positive (electron-deficient) part of a circuit whose current comes from a generator depends on the direction in which a moving coil cuts the lines of force in a magnetic field.

---

250. **When a single coil is rotated in a magnetic field, the current generated in the coil moves in one direction during one half of its rotation, in the other direction during the other half. What do we call a current of this type?**

Alternating current.

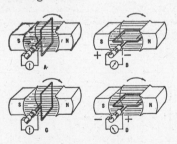

---

251. **What is direct current?**

Current which flows only in one direction—from one terminal of a battery or generator to the other.

252. How is the armature of a generator or magneto connected to the power lines of an electric circuit?

By means of sliding contacts, called brushes, which press against two separate rings on the shaft of the rotating coil. Each ring is connected to one side of the coil.

(NOTE: From this frame on, both magnetos and generators will be called "generators.")

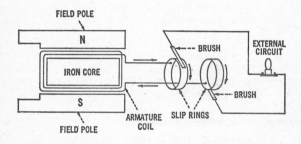

253. Since a revolving coil cuts a magnetic field in one direction during half of its revolution, and in the reverse direction during the other half of its revolution, what kind of current would we expect from a generator whose coil (armature) was connected through simple solid ring and brush contacts to a power line?

Alternating current.

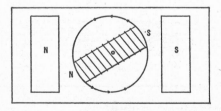

The current changes direction and reverses the polarity of the armature.

254. How can direct current be produced by a generator?

By replacing the two slip rings with two separated halfs of one ring (see illustration). Each half is connected to one side of the moving coil. Thus, when the current in the coil reverses its direction, the take-off connections are also reversed.

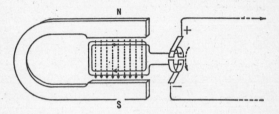

The commutator switches the polarity of the armature at the right instant to produce direct current in the external circuit.

255. If current from an outside power source is fed directly to the brushes of a generator, what behavior can we expect of the armature coil?

Because of the Oersted effect, the coil will tend to revolve.

256. If the generator is so designed that when current is fed continuously to the brushes of the generator the armature will revolve continuously, what do we then call the "generator"?

An electric motor.

257. What conclusion can we draw from this reversible electromechanical behavior of a generator?

The reverse of a motor is a generator, and the reverse of a generator is a motor. In one, electric current is turned into mechanical force; in the other, mechanical force is converted into electric current.

1. An electric current is generated in a coil of wire (solenoid) whenever a _____ is thrust through the coil (solenoid).

   _____[239]

2. If a _____ which has been thrust into a coil is then pulled out, a current is also generated, but this time the current moves in the _____ direction.

   _____[240]

3. A flow of _____ is generated in a wire (or a coil of wire) whenever the wire (or coil) is cut by a moving _____; or whenever the lines of a _____ are cut by the moving wire (or coil).

   _____[241]

4. This flow of _____ is reversed in direction if the direction of the moving element (either the magnet, if this is the moving element, or the wire or coil of wire) is reversed.

   _____[241]

5. If we rotate a coil of wire through a magnetic field, we generate an _____ in the coil of wire.

   _____[243]

6. A device that generates an electric current by rotating a coil of wire between the poles of a permanent magnet is called a _____.

   _____[244]

7. A device that generates an electric current by revolving a coil of wire between the poles of a(n) _____ is called an electric generator.

   _____[245]

8. The name armature is applied to a coil which revolves within the magnetic field of a _____ or an electric generator.

_____[248]

9. The direction of flow of an electric current through a coil revolving in a magnetic field depends on the _____ in which the coil cuts the lines of the field.

_____[249]

10. Electric current in which the direction of electron flows is reversed each time the coil of the generator completes a half turn is called _____ current.

_____[250]

11. The armature of a generator is connected to power lines by means of sliding contacts called _____, which press against two separate _____ connected to the ends of the armature coil.

_____[252]

12. To enable a generator to produce direct, rather than alternating current, it is necessary to replace the solid rings with half-rings, and so connect these that the direction of the current flow is reversed each half revolution of the

_____.

_____[254]

13. Because of the Oersted effect, an electric current passed through the armature coil of a generator will cause the armature to tend to _____.

_____[255]

14. An electric motor is essentially a _____ in which current, fed into the armature coil, causes the coil to

_____.

_____[256-257]

GENERAL REVIEW

1. A flow of electrons along or through a conductor is called a(n) _____ _____.

   _____[3]

2. We regard a piling up of electrons on a surface, or a deficiency of electrons on a surface (with respect to another surface), as an electric _____.

   _____[4]

3. Electrons are regarded as negative _____.

   _____[5]

4. A positive charge is a _____ of electrons on a surface (with respect to another surface).

   _____[8]

5. The chief structure of an atom consists of a(n) _____ around which _____ are assumed to move.

   _____[10]

6. Electrons that are only loosely bound to the _____ of an atom are called _____ electrons.

   _____[24]

7. Substances composed of atoms whose outer shell is less than half-filled are good _____ of electricity.

_____[26]

8. Two pith balls suspended side by side, both of which have been given a positive charge, will tend to _____ each other.

_____[52]

9. Coulomb's Law is used to calculate the amounts of _____ between two charged bodies.

_____[61]

10. The unit used to measure the quantity of an electric charge is the _____.

_____[63]

11. The ampere is the unit used to measure the _____ of an electric current.

_____[65]

12. The ohm is the electrical unit of _____.

_____[75]

13. In an electrical circuit, the relationship of volts, ohms, and amperes is expressed by a law known as _____.

_____[81-82]

14. An electromotive force of _____ volts will be required to operate a lamp that draws 3 amperes and has a resistance of 4 ohms.

_____[109]

15. If resistors of 3 ohms, 4 ohms, and 5 ohms, respectively, are connected in series, their combined resistance is _____ ohms.

_____[118]

16. If a 2 ohm resistor and a 3 ohm resistor are connected in parallel, their combined resistance is _____ ohms.

_____[130]

17. The common electrical unit of power is the _____.

_____[139]

18. An electric lamp operating at 12 volts and drawing a current of 2 amperes, has a power rating of _____ _____.

_____[143]

19. A 15 ampere fuse will melt when the current passing through it is _____ amperes, or more.

_____[155]

20. A kilowatt equals _____ watts.

_____[161]

21. How many 100 watt bulbs can be operated by a generator which has an output of 2 kilowatts?

_____[162]

22. The formula which shows the relation of amperage to watts is _____.

_____[166]

23. In a dry cell or storage battery, the electrode which has the greater number of free electrons is the _____ electrode.

_____[171]

24. The region around a magnet in which its force can be measured is called its _____.

_____[189]

25. The unit of magnetic flux is the _____.

_____[210]

26. The occurrence of a magnetic field around a wire which is activated by an electric current is called the _____ effect.

_____[219]

27. A solenoid which is equipped with a soft iron core is a(n) _____.

_____[237]

28. An electric generator is a device for creating an electric current by rotating a _____ between the poles of a(n) _____.

_____[245]

29. An electric current whose direction of flow is reversed with a certain frequency (such as 60 times per second) is called _____ current.

_____[250]

30. If an electric current of sufficient strength is connected to the coil of an electric generator, the generator will function as an electric _____.

_____[257]

GENERAL REVIEW: ANSWERS

1. Electric current
2. Charge
3. Particles
4. Deficiency
5. Nucleus, electrons
6. Nucleus, free
7. Conductors
8. Repel
9. Attraction (or repulsion)
10. Coulomb
11. Rate of flow
12. Resistance
13. Ohm's Law
14. 12
15. 12
16. 1.2
17. Watt
18. 24 watts
19. 15
20. 1000
21. 20
22. $I = \dfrac{P}{E}$
23. Negative
24. Magnetic field
25. Maxwell
26. Oersted
27. Electromagnet
28. Coil, electromagnet
29. Alternating
30. Motor